Prompt Me Again

Creative Writing Journal & Workbook

Prompt Me Series #4

◆

By
Robin Woods

Epic Books Publishing

A boutique publishing company
Visit us at: www.epicbookspublishing.com

Lead Editor: Beth Braithwaite
Additional Editing: Brooke E. Wayne

Copyright © 2018 Robin Woods
First Edition

Cover Design created on Canva by Robin Woods

All Photos taken by Robin Woods
Thanks to Tim, Jason, and Jenn for being my models.

Illustrations are public domain images from the 1800s provided by The British Museum

Fonts: Century, Gothic Ultra

Summary: A wide variety of writing prompts for maximum inspiration.

[Creative Writing, Diary, Non-Fiction, Reference, Writing Workbook, Fiction Writing, Writing Journal]

ISBN-10: 1-941077-12-9
ISBN-13: 978-1-941077-12-2

Table of Contents

Introduction

When taking pictures for this workbook, I came across this stacked wood in a wild array of colors. Part of it reminded me of a pile of books and the other part of an artist's palette—wild hues in haphazard designs that were used to create something else very beautiful. This is much like writing.

Writing is sometimes messy, and sometimes we need a little help even getting to the mess. When you begin to form your ideas, don't worry about grammar and punctuation. Simply getting the words down and experimenting is the most important part in the beginning. In order to become a better writer, you need to do three things:

1. Write often.

2. Read often.

3. Don't be afraid to make mistakes.

Embrace the mess, find your voice, and don't get discouraged. As Ray Bradbury once said:

> "You must stay drunk on writing so reality cannot destroy you."

Think of these pages as your artist's studio. Experiment with color and style. You never know; you may start something that grows into a masterpiece.

How to Use This Book

There are a variety of different styles of prompts in this workbook to help you decide what works best for you. If one style or prompt doesn't work, move on. If it doesn't work for you today, it might tomorrow.

If the pronouns don't work for you, change the she to a he, or vice versa. Prompts are meant to be inspiration, not shackles.

Carry it around with you. Mess it up. Use different kinds of ink. Stick Post-Its all over it.

Now, go forth and write!

Picture Prompts

It has often been said that a picture is worth a thousand words—but that doesn't really help writers. However, a picture can inspire thousands of words.

Use the following photos to create a unique story.

Writing Challenge:

Use at least three of the five senses in each of your stories—or add an extra sense.

☐ Sight ☐ Taste ☐ Touch ☐ Smell ☐ Hearing

The reference section in the back contains charts.

Picture Prompt How To

We are visual beings, so let's use our graphic nature to find inspiration. Following this page, you will find fifteen photo prompts. Use each of them as a muse for a story. It can be super short or the beginnings of a novel. Here is a sample of what to do. When I see this picture, it makes me think about ancient castles and secret potions. So here is my story:

I woke with my fingers twined in a fishing net and my arm wound around a faded life preserver. Every bone in my body protested as I sat up. The world seemed to list to the side for a moment, but I realized it was just me—not the world itself. The goose egg on my forehead told me that I probably had a concussion.

Standing on shaky legs, I walked woodenly towards a dune on the desolate beach. Caked sand from my hair tumbled over my shoulders with each agonizing step.

Cold air lashed at me, bringing with it the scent of burnt wood over the salt and seaweed. With effort, I trudged up the sandy hill, taking two steps forward, then sliding one back as I made my way to higher ground.

Once atop the dune, I turned a slow circle to survey the area. I was on an island and not one boat dotted the waters around me. I licked my parched lips and cringed when my lip split and the metallic taste of blood hit my tongue. The island couldn't be more than a dozen city blocks. A rocky outcrop poked up on the other side filled with lush trees, and from here, it looked as though water was streaming onto the beach from that area.

I had three pressing needs: water, shelter, and food. The rest I could figure out later. I didn't like the dark look of the clouds on the horizon. Releasing a shaky breath, I started my trek towards the area I hoped would provide all three. After a hundred yards of scratchy and prickly vegetation, I decided to cut back over the beach and find a friendly spot to reach the green oasis I had seen.

The hard-packed sand was welcoming as I threaded my way around the small island. My heart skipped a beat when I spotted a trunk on the sand around the bend. I picked up speed and half-trotted to the box. Heaving it open, I found some supplies. Fishing line, hooks, a knife, water purification tablets, and some dried jerky. With trembling hands, I snatched up the note in a plastic sleeve. "We had warned you to keep your mouth shut. This is on you." Hot tears plummeted down my cheeks—*it was true.*

1. Title: _____

2. Title: _____

3. Title: _____

4. Title: _____

5. Title: _____

6. Title: _____

7. Title: _____

8. Title: _____

9. Title: _____

10. Title: _____

11. Title: _____

12. Title: _____

13. Title: _____

14. Title: _____

15. Title: _____

Story Starters: First Person

Emotional Standpoint: Subjective
View: Limited
Pronoun Usage: I/we/us/me/my/mine/our/ours

Writing Challenge:

Limit the amount of times your character "felt" or "feels" something. Use active voice to help keep the reader in the experience.

First Person

16. Tucking a greasy strand of hair behind my ear, I prepared to…

17. The houses, streets, and businesses were all empty. Broken glass crunched under my feet as I backed into the alley, afraid I'd stayed too long.

18. Someone sloshed out of my tub. I froze. I didn't have any guests.

19. To my surprise, wet paint coated my fingertips. *Why?* Alarmed, I immediately spun in a circle to survey the room, but everything *seemed* to be in place…

20. I curled myself inward, feeling the sickness spread through my veins…

21. Cupping the offering in my hands, I approached the altar on catlike feet, praying that I wouldn't wake the…

22. Joy and relief washed over my senses, despite…

23. My stomach dropped to my feet and back again—it was all because of a single detail that I'd missed.

24. As my father stared down at me, all I could think was, "You failed me."

25. Drips of water rhythmically splatted on the limestone floor, lulling me like a metronome until I realized something was moving closer with each drip.

26. For a long moment I tried to wake up, but then I realized that this wasn't a dream.

27. The color sliding through my veins began to change; everyone would know in a matter of moments.

28. I couldn't shove the food into my mouth fast enough…

29. Sickness curled in my gut the moment I realized that everything the seer had told me was wrong.

30. When she took my hand, I felt a network of electricity surge through me…

31. "You're firing me?" I cried. Behind my back, I slid the thumb drive into my back pocket and forced tears into my eyes.

32. I wasn't sure what that thing was, but she certainly wasn't my mother.

33. "This is how you have been doing it? Drugging people?" A scoffing sound escaped my throat as I popped to my feet and…

34. The fine, yellow powder filtered through my fingers, becoming mist…

35. He was still in my head, somehow I knew the safe combination.

36. Keeping this secret was getting harder and harder. I kept replaying the lost expression on his face as I remained silent, but I knew telling would...

37. I rubbed at my eyes. This couldn't be...they had all died over a year ago.

38. My phone buzzed in my pocket for the fifth time in the last three minutes. I prayed that they wouldn't hear it. There was no way that I could...

39. They thought I was asleep. It was hard not to grin as I removed...

40. I told myself one last time, "No one will know it's missing." The only problem was that it was a lie. A lie that could get people killed.

41. My heart thundered when the eyes in the painting blinked. I wasn't alone.

42. After the manicurist clipped my nails, she surreptitiously slipped them into her pocket when she thought I wasn't looking. *Why did she have to do something so stupid?*

43. *This was the worst vacation ever*, she thought. Two days...

44. "Cowards," I growled under my breath. The sun was setting, so I didn't have long until...

45. The metal felt cool in my hand despite having used...

46. When I opened my door, once again, dead flowers were carefully placed on my welcome mat. *These were so not welcome.*

47. Holding my breath, I stepped into the bathroom. It was...

48. The tree stretched into the sky, blotting out the sun in this entire quadrant. Trembling and swallowing hard, I realized it was time. So I began to climb...

49. Droplets splattered on the wet paint, leaving a terrifying...

50. "Why does it have to be robots?" I complained. Choking down the rest of my grumble, I clasped his elbow and moved...

51. Nailing the last board into place, I leaned against the creaking structure, wanting...

52. The package was jammed inside the mailbox. When it came loose, I went flying backwards, landing hard on my tailbone and spilling the contents of the box...

53. It was nice to see him smile again, but it made this much more painful.

54. When I heard the click, I exhaled, readying to...

55. The way the water swallowed me up was almost as bad as the way his lies had done the same.

56. He sprayed the fire-retardant on me. "How well does this work?" I asked.

57. I rubbed my brow before confirming, "You want me to crawl into the air vent and release those," motioning to the canister, "and get out alive?"

58. "I'm not even a little bit okay," I spat, glaring into the darkness.

59. "It's not my fault," I repeated over and over again. But deep down, I knew I may not have been responsible for everything, but I'd toppled the first domino when...

60. Heaving a breath, I finally admitted, "I get why she chose you."

61. Clutching the weapon, I trembled with the realization, *I was becoming the monster I was trying so hard to destroy.*

62. Waves pounded the dock relentlessly, making me wonder if this was a good idea...

63. "It's a board game! How was I supposed to know that if we lose money in the game, it happens in real life?" I stumbled backwards away from...

64. "You prayed for patience?" I grinned. "Yeah, I'm praying for a rocket launcher."

65. Grabbing the wheel, I heaved it with everything I had while the crowd watched. I could feel collective breaths being held as...

66. The serum hadn't worked. I remembered everything...

67. They sat at the same table, but it was apparent that all of them were lost to their devices. I disconnected my eyepiece, knowing I had plenty of time before...

68. Like an elixir, happiness enraptured me to the point I couldn't see anything...

69. He grabbed my wrist and said, "I made a deal with the devil, sweetheart, and you are my offering."

70. Sobs stuck in my chest, rocking my body in wretched convulsions as the...

71. What sounded like rain created a pitter-patter on the roof, but when I looked out the window, I realized it wasn't rain...

72. It was apparent that he wasn't my prince, and I sure wasn't a princess...

73. At first, I thought they were angels, but there was something off. I took a step back, realizing that their wings were...

74. When my phone rang at midnight, I knew it could only mean...

75. I wondered how long it would take people until they realized I was dead. I mean, the smell I was emitting should have tipped them off a while ago, but they kept smiling at me...

Prompt # _____ Your Title: _____

Prompt # _____ Your Title: _____

Prompt # _____ Your Title: _____

Prompt # _____ Your Title: _____

Prompt # _____ Your Title: _____

Prompt # _____ Your Title: _____

Prompt # _____ Your Title: _____

Prompt # _____ Your Title: _____

Prompt # _____ Your Title: _____

Story Starters: Third Person

Third Person Limited
Emotional Standpoint: Objective
View: Limited
Pronoun Usage: he/she/it/him/his/her/they/their

Third Person Omniscient
Emotional Standpoint: Objective
View: Unlimited
Pronoun Usage: he/she/it/him/his/her/they/their

Deep Third Person
Emotional Standpoint: Subjective
View: Limited
Pronoun Usage: he/she/it/him/his/her/they/their

Writing Challenge:

Vary your language, especially your sentence openings. I.e. Not every sentence in your paragraph should begin with "The" or "Then."

Third Person

76. The groan of ice jarred the ship. Soon they would be free to…

77. He sprang from his hiding place and seized the elixir faster than a jackrabbit riding a rocket. The smile slipped from his face when…

78. She tore the yellowed flyer down and crumpled it into a jagged ball.

79. She sobbed over the sink, "I'm like Lady Macbeth. No matter how much water I use, I can't wash these stains away."

80. There was no way to know how strong the enemy was on the other side of the gate, so…

81. After a long moment, the tattoo began to burn. He screamed, "This wasn't part of the bargain!"

82. His eyes were too watchful. His gaze too penetrating. He was up to no good.

83. He pushed the glasses up his nose with one hand, and with the other hand, he clutched the wand in his pocket. They would…

84. A blush bloomed across her cheeks, and he found it only made him fancy her more.

85. Small children laughed, dragging a burlap bag behind them. Then he realized, those weren't children and something was moving inside the bag.

86. He tugged at his sleeve to keep the scars hidden, but it was too late…

87. She looked at him with a morbid sort of expression, a burst of words escaping her painted lips, "I'm the author of my own destruction. Can't you see?"

88. He gazed at the night sky, and the stars seemed to whisper, "Move on."

89. As the fan blade made a chopping sound, each spin drove him closer and closer to madness. He had survived extermination, but the fan was what was making him lose it.

90. Everyday the impossible happens, yet none of them believed that the next moment…

91. Most murders have something to do with pride, love, money, or grief—but this was not the case. This killer was creating…

92. She didn't worry until the rain started to burn. Then, she set to…

93. Ravens were squawking at the new arrivals. There was a reason that a group of crows was called a 'murder.'

94. The answers were in the photograph. Six faded faces mocked her as she peered at the snapshot.

95. They thought she was bulletproof, but she was way more than that...

96. Rings from two glasses left on the coffee table were etched into the surface. He was toast when his mom got home...

97. He was running late again. She hated that. Swallowing her anger, she...

98. "Is that a body on the back patio?" She didn't wait for an answer, but rather shrugged and wandered into the kitchen to make tea. Her lack of...

99. The plume of smoke changed from white to black as it drifted...

100. There were way too many buyers interesting in the property. They must have done something wrong—or something was about to go wrong.

101. He smeared the war paint across her cheeks and nose with trembling fingers.

102. Cardboard contaminated with the smell of manure permeated her car. She gasped, trying not to taste it. This was the last time she would...

103. Taking shallow breaths, the old woman leaned over the railing, grabbing his...

104. "Did he just squeal and faint at the sight of his own blood?" she asked the team, seconds before all of them burst out with laughter.

105. Hitting pause, she strained to listen...

106. She had been told not to look into her family history, but she didn't believe that she would find anything except a boring line of unexceptional people just like her.

107. He bristled. "Is that a threat?" he asked, as his hand moved to his pocket.

108. The lump in the tire was growing larger. They didn't have long until it would blow out, then it would take...

109. Curls spiraled over her shoulders, bobbing with each pretty step until she reached...

110. She was weary of burying her friends night after night. She sighed and rubbed at her forehead with the back of her hand. She wouldn't do it next time they asked.

111. This was against his rules. *No children.* He swayed on his feet making the decision.

112. A slow awareness unfurled before him. The parents who had raised him his entire life were imposters.

113. The night before was all a blur...taking aspirin and then later, swinging a bat.

114. She had managed to keep her identity hidden for over a decade. No one looked too closely at the chubby beggar on the corner who slipped into the forest at dusk.

115. The judge raised an arched brow. "Darling, everyone thinks that they are innocent."

116. A water-stained note fell to the ground when she picked up her crumpled jacket.

117. Someone tapped her on the shoulder. She turned and stared blankly at the stranger. Then he said, "Didn't anyone ever tell you that eavesdropping can be fatal?"

118. When his mom appeared with the sheriff, he knew he was in for it.

119. Wrapping his hand with great care, his mother's words repeated in his head. "It's not a good idea to keep that thing as a pet."

120. He closed the door, looking at the wild-eyed thing in the corner. "There, there," he cooed.

121. She glanced behind her, bare feet slapping on the pavement. Even more dogs were following her down the tree-lined way.

122. The room came swimming into focus—*it had worked.* She stumbled forward to save...

123. She observed that the entry was paved with skulls, but it didn't make her break her stride as she headed towards...

124. A horrible chortle erupted from him before he said, "That's going the leave a mark."

125. Rolling the corpse off the top of him, he checked side-to-side to make sure they were gone. A sob caught in his throat, but he shoved it down knowing he had only minutes.

126. After the blow to the head, she woke with a new clarity—everyone was lying to her.

127. He held out his hand to catch the delicate snow falling soundlessly to earth, but then he realized that it wasn't snow—it was millions of tiny, dead insects.

128. "I'm sorry," he murmured, backing away from the locked capsule.

129. The melodic voice of the therapist lulled him into a state of relaxation, but this time, when she thought he was under, he was awake. He had to know his trigger.

130. "One more complaint, and I'll pop you one," he barked, but he was alone.

131. A lump caught in her throat. "You realize that I can't actually heal people, right? I can simply give your wounds to someone else."

132. She grabbed his collar and spoke through clenched teeth, "Act human."

133. Groaning, he rubbed at his head, wondering who in the room had hit him. *It sure wasn't Colonel Mustard with the candlestick.*

134. His frustration was volcanic; he couldn't decide if he wanted to kiss her or kill her.

135. Mandatory vaccinations had been in place for over a decade, but they hadn't foreseen that it would cause infertility in everyone who had received the shots.

136. They had made it to dawn, but the screeching behind them said that they weren't safe.

Prompt # _____ Your Title: _____

Prompt # _____ Your Title: _____

Prompt # _____ Your Title: _____

Prompt # _____ Your Title: _____

Prompt # _____ Your Title: _____

Use These Phrases

Writing Challenge:

Writers often forget to incorporate the sense of smell into their writings. Try to use this sense in an offbeat way. A chart is in the back to help with inspiration.

137. Choose and use at least six of these ten phrases:

rapturous delight	state of bliss
dread weighing	like dry, skeletal leaves
hammering heart	looked effortlessly easy
brutal disagreement	smug shrug of the shoulders
salacious grin	voice had an uncharacteristic hitch

138. Choose and use at least seven of these ten phrases:

sharp scent of pine	velvet, darkness of night
amusement curled her lip	the hollow drip of water
intricate stained-glass windows	scrunched his button nose
iridescent spots of light	throaty laughter
rhythm of waves	veiled in cobwebs

139. Choose and use at least eight of these ten phrases:

smartly dressed	like liquid crystals
bathed in amber light	lips crinkled in distaste
rapid thrum of her heart	monotonously moved up and down
honey-sweet fragrance	graffiti-covered buildings
dust filtered down	ironed her hips with her hands

140. Choose and use at least nine of these ten phrases:

jagged spires of rock	vibrant spots of color
delicious freedom	dynamic change in weather
vigorous run	happy shriek
thundering feet	irreverent youth
cloying smell of wet pavement	wriggle through

141. Choose and use at least nine of these ten phrases:

tang sparking her senses	rough grind of grit
flutter of wings	blotting out the sun
deafening roar	breeze through
authentic belly laugh	stitched together by madness
squelch of thick mud	shadow encased

Prompt # _____ Your Title: _____

Choose a Path

Writing Challenge:

Use at least three of the five senses in each of your stories.

☐ Sight ☐ Sound ☐ Hearing ☐ Taste ☐ Touch

If your story has fantasy elements, you can always add a sixth sense.

142. With skill, she pulled out a knife and...

- ☐ slathered a thick coat of butter on the coarse bread.
- ☐ chipped away at the plaster around the rusty, iron bars.
- ☐ carved the turkey under the watchful eyes of the refugees.
- ☐ used it to start the aging, muscle car.
- ☐ began the autopsy, feeling that she wasn't going to like the answers.

143. He slammed the door behind him, knowing that...

- ☐ he only had seconds before the assassins would be on him again.
- ☐ this was the last time he would see his family.
- ☐ the fire would soon consume the last of his past.
- ☐ he was tarnishing everything he had created.
- ☐ he had to make sure they saw him leave—or it would ruin everything.

144. **Her control was slipping as she...**

- ☐ piloted the shuttle into the open water to avoid collateral damage.
- ☐ injected herself with the antidote.
- ☐ watched her attacker enter the room to taunt her.
- ☐ faced the judge, knowing she was innocent.
- ☐ tried not to cry out from the pain.

145. **Candles flickered throughout when the door blew open and...**

☐ the man in black entered with some swagger.

☐ snow tumbled into the feverish room, keeping it open.

☐ revealed a gang armed with chains and crowbars.

☐ the mountain lion prowled inside.

☐ the cry of a stranger brought the wedding to a halt.

146. Sparks sputtered from the...

- ☐ rim after the tire blew.
- ☐ grinder as a breach team positioned themselves to rush inside.
- ☐ fireworks, but no one was left to see the spectacle.
- ☐ comet streaking through the darkened sky.
- ☐ electrical panel that was dangerously close to the oxygen tanks.

147. Absolute terror flooded through the...

- ☐ participants as Nightmare Serum was pumped into their veins.
- ☐ crowd as zombies burst through the blockade.
- ☐ city when they realized Zeus was real—and he was back.
- ☐ animals at the sound of the first gunshot.
- ☐ children when they realized their parents had lied about being safe.

Dialogue Prompts

A few tips before we start:

- ☐ Avoid using the characters' names too much in dialogue.
- ☐ Make sure not all of your characters sound the same.
- ☐ Try not to have characters parrot or repeat the previous sentence.

Writing Challenge:

Use as few adverbs as possible.

- ☐ Generally, people don't speak in complete sentences. Use some fragments.
- ☐ Play with dialect and the way your characters use contractions.
- ☐ Restarts, stumbles, and stutters can improve emotional scenes.

148. "You've earned a good time," she nodded.

"Soooo, I didn't deserve it based on my sparkling personality?"

"Oh, you will get what you deserve."

149. The crone handed him a fragile porcelain cup with gnarled hands. "Drink this, and see no more monsters."

He raised it to his lips, then paused. "See no more monsters? Does that mean that they're really there?"

150. "Your house is haunted?"

"It's totally fine. She's a nice old lady who reads to me when I go to sleep."

151. "Can you go be stupid somewhere else?"

"I'm only stupid when I'm around you. It must be contagious."

152. "I don't want them to feel a thing."

"You aren't in a position to make requests."

153. "Should I be worried that we seem to be headed towards certain doom?"

"Only if you forgot money for the meter."

154. "Take that *thing* off if you are going to speak to me."

"Then there will be nothing to protect you."

155. "He wasn't what I'd expected."

"Did you expect horns and a pitchfork?"

More dialogue prompts...

156. "You only get two more wishes, and then I go back in the lamp."

   "Cute."

157. "You are not alone in your sorrow. Allow yourself to grieve, for there is no shame or weakness in it."

   "I will grieve when I find justice for what was done."

158. "You kidnap me, and you want me to say thank you?"

   "I would call it 'borrowing.'"

159. "Do you want to be free of your pain?" he asked, his voice like silk.

   "Actually, I've gotten a little attached to it."

160. "I'll flip you for it."

   "We are talking about the fate of the world, not what movie to go to."

   "Meh. I just want you to think that you actually have a chance."

161. "Is that a spider?"
   "Yeah. And about a million of his friends. Run!"

162. "I believe that is my seat."

   "Funny. I seem to be wearing the crown."

Prompt # _____ Your Title: _____

Fill in the Blank: 49 Possibilities

163. The ___ marched in an endless ___.

Blank One	Blank Two
soldiers	line past the horizon
ants	campaign to get to the picnic
inmates	series of chaotic events
ideas	night filled with possibilities
workers	wave into the darkness
elephants	summer brimming with ripe fruits
children	stream, swirling inside her head

164. Buildings filled with ___ needed to ___.

Blank One	Blank Two
debris	be cashed in
office workers	cleared
prisoners	exterminated
treasure	be brought to life
weapons	evacuated
mannequins	be moved to a secure facility
rodents	give their reports to admin

165. The ___ went ___ into the night.

Blank One	Blank Two
spaceship	soaring
hunter	stalking
leopard	floating
drone	curiously
ghost	spiraling
dinosaur	scampering
toddler	recklessly forward

166. Water spewed from the ___ and ___.

Blank One	Blank Two
dam	washed the docks south
reserve tanks	left the survivors without water
faucet	rinsed the filth away
falls	flooded the valley
levee	doused the flames
fire engine	enveloped the trucks
sink hole	the crowd cheered in thanks

Prompt # _____ Your Title: _____

It's Your Choice

Writing Challenge:

Give your character a secret that influences all of his or her decisions.

Choose Your Noun

man	woman	child	teenager	convict
priest	politician	surfer	student	barista
cow	dog	horse	tiger	kangaroo
dragon	dinosaur	unicorn	mammoth	griffin

167. "Didn't I tell you to make sure the __ didn't bother the neighbors?"

168. "That ___ is running for office again. How is that even possible?"

Broken

169. Broken ___ ____ into ____.

noun	verb	direct object
girls	blossom	leaders
boys	transformed	warriors
animals	are molded	servants
machines	are honed	prisoners

Choose Who and When

170. What if your character was raised by ___ in the year ___.

doctors	cave people	1492	900 AD
lions	carnival workers	1666	1790
detectives	a seer	1929	1934
mercenaries	chimney sweeps	1956	1988
mole people	fairies	1990	2050

That's Classic

Writing Challenge:

Use the character awareness chart in the reference section to add insights to what your character is reacting to.

War & Peace

Use these famous lines from Niccolo Machiavelli and Mother Teresa to be the guiding ideology of a character. Machiavelli is the perfect template for an antagonist or an anti-hero. Mother Teresa's guidance is fabulous for a virtuous protagonist, the wise side-kick, or a sage elder.

WAR—Niccolo Machiavelli Quotes

171. "Men ought either to be indulged or utterly destroyed, for if you merely offend them they take vengeance, but if you injure them greatly they are unable to retaliate, so that the injury done to a man ought to be such that vengeance cannot be feared."

172. "It is better to be feared than loved, if you cannot be both."

173. "And if, to be sure, sometimes you need to conceal a fact with words, do it in such a way that it does not become known, or, if it does become known, that you have a ready and quick defense."

174. "Only those means of security are good, are certain, are lasting, that depend on yourself and your own vigor."

175. "One who deceives will always find those who allow themselves to be deceived."

176. "Never was anything great achieved without danger."

177. "I'm not interested in preserving the status quo; I want to overthrow it."

PEACE—Mother Teresa Quotes

178. "Let us always meet each other a with smile, for the smile is the beginning of love."

179. "We cannot do great things on this Earth, only small things with great love."

180. "People are unreasonable, illogical, and self-centered. Love them anyway."

181. "One of the greatest diseases is to be nobody to anybody."

182. "If you can't feed a hundred people, then just feed one."

183. "Love begins by taking care of the closest ones—the ones at home."

184. "I know the power obedience has of making things easy which seem impossible."

185. "Don't let your sins turn into bad habits."

186. "One must really have suffered oneself to help others."

187. "Our souls may lose their peace and even disturb other people's, if we are always criticizing trivial actions—which often are not real defects at all, but we construe them wrongly through our ignorance of their motives."

Prompt #_____ Your Title: _____

Fairy Tale Elements

Fairy tales across the world share certain elements. The following is a list of common traits. If you would like to give your story some added depth, incorporate some of these.

☐ **Set in the past**
> Once upon a time...
> A long time ago...

☐ **Often takes place in a distant land**
> In a realm on the other side of the world...
> In a galaxy far, far away...

☐ **Clearly defined good characters and evil characters**
> Villain versus hero (and maybe a fairy or three)
> Evil queen after the innocent princess

☐ **May include magic and spells**
> Magic may be positive or negative
> Evil wizard bent on domination versus a good wizard who loves all

☐ **Personification**
> A mirror that can talk
> Mice or birds who can help

☐ **Often includes objects, people, or events in threes and sevens**
> Three wishes
> Repeat a name three times
> Three blind mice
> Seven dwarves

☐ **The plot revolves around a problem or conflict that needs to be solved**

☐ **The conflict or problem is resolved in a positive way**

☐ **Usually teaches a lesson or demonstrates values of the culture**

☐ **Happy ending...they lived happily ever after**

Fairy Tale Mash Up

Write a short story of adventure and intrigue. Try to incorporate lots of threes and sevens.

188. A princess who falls asleep whenever the prince kisses her.

189. A giant plants a beanstalk that grows into the clouds and a boy climbs down it.

190. A dragon who saves the princess from a knight.

191. A child wishes for parents and is given animal caretakers.

192. A beautiful boy has an evil stepfather and is saved by the kind princess.

193. A girl goes to a ball and has to solve three riddles to avoid the affections of the prince.

194. A goose is convinced that a girl can lay golden eggs and follows her everywhere.

195. A magical owl assists a boy with his wolf problem.

196. An adventurous girl leaves home to break a curse by finding a magical ring.

197. A courageous princess must slay a monster to save her brother and acquire a magical mirror.

198. A queen and king didn't fulfill their promise and are turned into frogs.

199. A daring boy escapes a dragon and finds himself in a mine with dwarves.

200. A princess doesn't kiss the frog because she likes having a talking amphibian friend.

201. The king decides the neighboring prince is an idiot and cancels the wedding.

202. The princess feels the pea under the mattress, but instead, tells the maid where it is.

203. Little Red Riding Hood is a huntress in search of wolves.

204. Goldilocks is really a cat burglar.

205. Sleeping Beauty is only pretending to sleep.

206. The Seven Dwarves are gangsters.

207. They put Humpty Dumpty back together, but he wasn't the same.

208. The Three Little Pigs *wanted* the wolf to go to the brick house.

209. Take any fairy or folk tale and add monsters.

210. Take a fairy tale character and plop them into a different fairy tale world.

*Illustration from
The British Museum*

Fairy Tale Plot Practice

Lesson to teach:

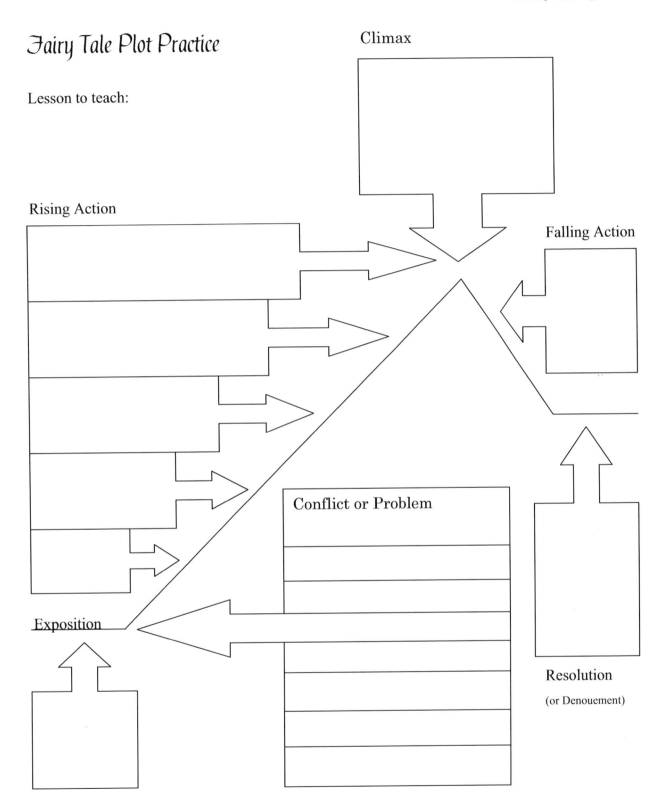

Climax

Rising Action

Falling Action

Conflict or Problem

Exposition

Resolution

(or Denouement)

Prompt # _____ Your Title: _____

Illustrated

Use the following illustrations from classic books written in the 1800s to create an all-new story.

211. *Title:* _____

212. **Title:** _____

213. **Title:** _____

Prompt # _____ Your Title: _____

Traditional Prompts

Self-Discovery

Many of these are twists on well-worn topics, but creativity can spring from old favorites. These may help unlock something inside yourself, serve as interview questions, or help develop a character background.

214. What would you want on your tombstone?

215. Write about attending an event that you didn't want to attend (graduation, wedding, etc.). Why didn't you want to attend? Were you glad that you did in the end?

216. If money didn't exist, what would you do with your time?

217. You have been given an entire planet. What would your personal planet be like? Who would live there? Use all the senses in your description.

218. Besides family members, who has influenced you most in your life?

219. Has someone ever given you a small bit of advice or asked a question that has haunted you? If so, what was it? Why did it make such an impact?

220. What would you do if you knew that you could not fail?

221. If you could make ten rules about yourself that others would have to follow, what would they be?

222. If you could make ten rules for everyone on the planet, what would they be?

223. What fears do you want to overcome? What is your plan to conquer this fear? Or is there a fear that you already overcame? If so, tell the tale using descriptive language.

224. What do you regret NOT doing?

225. If you had the ability to create a clone of yourself, would you do it? How would you use the clone to your advantage?

226. List five small things and five large things for which you are thankful.

227. If you could have lunch with a fictional character or historical figure, who would you pick? Why? What would you want to do during the meeting? What would you ask?

228. What are the values, morals, and ethics you live by?

229. Make a list of things that you can control and cannot control. How do these things make you feel? Does trying to control the uncontrollable help or hurt you?

Prompt # _____ Your Title: _____

If You Were

If you were ___, who/what would you be? Explain by telling a story, using vivid verbs and sensory images.

230. a door

231. a piece of mail

232. a light switch

233. a muddy shoe

234. the sunrise (or sunset)

235. sunglasses

236. a lost penny

237. a dishrag

238. a balloon

239. a dumbbell

240. a security camera

241. an earring

242. a squirrel

243. ice cream

244. an aspirin

245. stained glass

246. a carnival mask

247. a tiara

248. a knife

249. sugary cereal or extra healthy cereal

250. a hotel room

251. a catfish

252. a knee brace

253. an ATM

254. a drug sniffing dog

Prompt # _____ Your Title: _____

Mixed Bag

A little mix of everything to keep it interesting.

255. A cursed lottery ticket.

256. A mirror that lends no reflection of the person standing before it, but rather their death.

257. A nightmare door—you decide what that means.

258. A snack food that takes a minute of life for each bite consumed—it's the most amazing tasting substance on the planet.

259. A piece of jewelry that carries the soul of all its past owners.

260. Astronauts discover a cave on Mars with ancient statues of Genghis Kahn, Alexander the Great, and Napoleon made from the natural rock of the planet.

261. A new technology permits us to faze through solid objects. Chaos ensues.

262. A contact lens that allows you to see through the veil into other realms parallel with our own.

263. Everyone in town is required to wear a mask by law.

264. Your character tries to say something in Latin, but instead summons the ghost of a former world leader. How does your character take advantage?

265. The water for an entire metropolitan area is going to run out in a week.

266. Your character has been married for fifteen years and finds out that their spouse is a clone.

267. Everyone on the planet with blue eyes suddenly drops dead.

268. For generations, all of the children in a community were born at sunrise. When a child is born at midnight, instantly everything changes.

269. A pill that grants people to change their skin color like a chameleon.

270. The Timeslipper had been causing havoc for a long while, but they had stranded him in 1963.

Prompt # _____ Your Title: _____

Rules and Proverbs

Your character or society live by a set of rules. Pick a few to support your world. Maybe your character is over-attached or interprets the proverb in the wrong way, and it leads to ruin. Have fun with it.

Variation: Flip the proverb around to say the opposite. For example, "love is power" can be twisted to "love is weakness."

271. Strength without mercy is meaningless.

272. Cheat the devil and tell the truth.

273. Compassion is life.

274. Question everything.

275. Family first.

276. Listening is power.

277. Discretion is the greater part of valor.

278. They tried to bury us. They did not know we were seeds.

279. Examine the actions and be wary of words.

280. All is fair in love and war.

281. Power corrupts. Absolute power corrupts absolutely.

282. Strike while the iron is hot.

283. A beautiful thing is never perfect.

284. Better alone than in bad company.

285. Do not push the river, it will flow by itself.

286. Fall seven times, stand up eight.

287. Drop by drop you break the rock.

Prompt # _____ Your Title: _____

Prompt # _____ Your Title: _____

Prompt # _____ Your Title: _____

Prompt # _____ Your Title: _____

Prompt # _____ Your Title: _____

Cinquain

A Practice in Brevity

Writing Challenge:

Diversify your topics and include a cinquain: about a friend, a family member, and something romantic. Then tap into some emotions: happiness, sadness, indifference, and need.

Cinquains are structured five-line poems and are a great way to practice precise language. There are many forms of the poems. Here are a few:

	Word Count	Syllable Count	Parts of Speech
Line 1	1 word	2 syllables	Noun
Line 2	2 words	4 syllables	2 adjectives
Line 3	3 words	6 syllables	3 gerunds (-ing)
Line 4	4 words	8 syllables	A phrase
Line 5	1 word	2 syllables	Synonym of line 1

Here are a couple of samples.

Word Count:

Loneliness [1]
Clocks ticking, [2]
Like icy fingers. [3]
Cold, damp gravestones [4]
Death. [1]

—Robin Woods

Parts of Speech:

Autumn. [2]
Cool breeze. [4]
Fluttering, drifting, landing. [6]
Papery thin leaves in brilliant color. [8]
Fall. [2]

—Robin Woods

288. About love:

_____
_____
_____
_____
_____

289. About loss:

_____
_____
_____
_____
_____

290. About joy:

_____
_____
_____
_____
_____

291. About friendship:

_____

_____

_____

_____

_____

292. About the city:

_____

_____

_____

_____

_____

293. Your choice:

_____

_____

_____

_____

_____

Journal

Reference

Facial Expressions

It is always best to come up with your own descriptions, but sometimes looking over a list can be inspiring. Use these as your catapult.

Eyes	Mouth	Nose
tears beaded in the corners crinkled in the corners glossy with tears liquid shimmered liquid-lined lashes pricked from oncoming pupils dilated tear-crusted eyes tears leapt from tears pooled on the rim welled to the brim wide as saucers eyelids drooped	audibly popped open brittle smile faded curved in a wicked grin expression wilted flashed teeth lopsided grin mouth twisted patience-worn smile pressed lips in a fine line rolled lips inward thin-lipped scowl snapped shut went slack	bunny-like nose sniffled crinkled with distaste flared with alertness huffed through nostrils nostril bulged petulantly sniffed pinched the bridge pushed glasses up red from alcohol scrunched at the stench sniffed arrogantly twitched in suspicion wiped furiously
batted, bulged, burned, darted, flashed, flickered, fluttered, glanced, glinted, leered, narrowed, rolled, sparked, squinted, swam, tearful, twinkled, weepy	beamed, bit, fell, grinned, ground, lopsided, popped open, pouted, puckered, pursed, rolled inward, smiled, smirked, snapped, twisted, twitched, quirked	bubbled, dripped, covered, crusted, gurgled, inhaled, puffed, sneered, snorted, sniveled, snored, tipped upwards, whistled, wrinkled, wriggled
Brows	Jaw	Other:
cocked a brow drew together jumped in surprise pinned together rose gradually seemed to collapse snapped together worry-line deepened	a teeth-shattering clench jaw dropped jowl smoothed jutted in defiance muscles jumped quivered with stress stiffened in expectation slide back and forth	
arched, collapsed, creased, crumpled, furrowed, knitted, lined, meld, puckered, raked, rose, slant, sink, wagged	clenched, cracked, flexed, jumped, jutted, pointed, popped, quivered, set, tensed, tightened, twitched	

Character Appearance Charts

Eye Color	Blue	Sky Blue	Baby Blue	Electric Blue	Cornflower
	Brown	Chestnut	Chocolate	Cognac	Amber
	Green	Sea Green	Moss Green	Jade	Emerald
	Grey	Silver	Gunmetal Grey	Charcoal	Black
	Hazel	Russet	Nut	Honey	Yellow
	Lavender	Other:			
Eye Shape	Almond	Round	Drooping	Hooded	Close-Set
	Wide-Set	Deep-Set	Protruding	Sleepy	Squinting
	Down-Turned	Other:			
Skin Tone	Fair	Ivory	Porcelain	Milky	Snow
	Ruddy	Rose	Peach	Ochre	Golden
	Olive	Khaki	Toffee	Honey	Tawny
	Dark	Ebony	Sepia	Russet	Mahogany
	Other:				
Body Shape	Triangle	Rectangle	Hourglass	Rounded	Diamond
	Inverted Triangle	Barrel	Willowy	Husky	Wiry
	Other:				
Facial Shapes	Oval	Rectangle	Square	Heart	Oblong
	Egg	Diamond	Triangle	Narrow	Block-Like
	Other:				
Hair Color	Black	Dark Brown	Medium Brown	Ash Brown	Golden Brown
	Red	Auburn	Copper	Strawberry	Cinnamon
	Blond	Platinum	White	Silver	Grey
	Other:				

Notes:

Survival Rules

SURVIVAL Rule of 3s

3 minutes
without air

3 hours
without shelter
in an extreme environment

3 days
without water

30 days
without food

3 months
without hope

30% of
your blood
After 40% it is fatal
without a transfusion.

30 minutes
in water 35 degrees

"Fever—Myths versus Facts." Seattle
Children's Hospital. 2017.
"Limits of the Human Body."
SurvivalLife.com WebMD.com

Fever over 103
for more than 3 days
Brain damage at 108,
heat stroke is fatal.

Words for Sounds

Add appeal to your writing by making a splash with descriptive sound words.

Ahem	Clatter	Grind	Pound	Splash	Tweet
Baa	Click	Groan	Pow	Splat	Vroom
Babble	Clink	Gulp	Pulsing	Splinter	Wail
Bang	Clomp	Gurgle	Purr	Sputter	Wallop
Bark	Clonk	Guzzle	Quack	Squawk	Whack
Beat	Clop	Hammer	Racket	Squeak	Wheeze
Beep	Cluck	Hiss	Rap	Squish	Whicker
Bellow	Clunk	Hoot	Ratchet	Stomp	Whinny
Blare	Crackle	Howl	Rattle	Suck	Whip
Blast	Crash	Hubbub	Revved	Swish	Whir
Blip	Creak	Hum	Ring	Swoop	Whisper
Blop	Crinkle	Jangle	Rip	Swoosh	Whistle
Blow	Crunch	Jingle	Roar	Tap	Whiz
Boing	Din	Kerplunk	Rumble	Tatter	Woof
Bong	Ding	Knock	Rushing	Tee-Hee	Woot
Boo	Discord	Lash	Rustle	Throb	Yap
Boom	Drip	Mew	Scream	Thud	Yawp
Bop	Drone	Mewl	Screech	Thump	Yelp
Bray	Drum	Murmur	Scuff	Thunder	Yip
Bubble	Eek	Neigh	Shriek	Thwack	Yowl
Burp	Fanfare	Oink	Shuffle	Tick	Zap
Buzz	Fizz	Ooze	Sizzle	Tinkle	Zip
Cacophony	Fizzle	Patter	Slam	Titter	Zoom
Cha-Ching	Flick	Peal	Slap	Tock	
Cheep	Fling	Peep	Slop	Tolling	Other:
Chime	Flop	Pew	Slurp	Toot	
Chirp	Fracas	Pitter-Patter	Smack	Trill	
Chug	Giggle	Plink	Snap	Tromp	
Clack	Glug	Plod	Snicker	Trumpet	
Clamor	Glurp	Plop	Snigger	Tsk	
Clang	Gnashing	Plunk	Snip	Tumult	
Clank	Gobble	Poof	Snort	Tut	
Clap	Grating	Pop	Spatter	Twang	

Character Awareness—Five Senses & Beyond

Sight	Taste	Location
Color	Astringent	**Geographically**—city, mountains, land, and sea
Depth	Bitter	
Motion	Salty	**Spatially**—what is your character near
Position	Savory	
Shape	Sour	**Security**—entrances, exits, windows, etc.
Size	Spicy	
Solidity	Sweet	**Communications**—phones, intercoms, alarms, etc.
Stillness	Umami	
Volume	*(See list of Tastes & Aromas)*	

Smell	Touch	Sound
Aromatic	Bumpy	Amplitude
Ash	Dryness	Base
Bitterness	Electrical charge	Cadence
Chemicals	Friction	Duration
Citrus	Gravity	Echo
Cold	Hardness	Frequency
Danger	Moisture	Monophonic
Decay	Oiliness	Pitch
Dust	Organic material	Polyphonic
Electricity	Pain	Reverberation
Fish	Pressure	Rhythm
Floral	Sharpness	Sonic texture
Freshness	Slimy	Sound decay
Fruity	Smooth	Sound intensity
Fungus	Softness	Sound power
Green	Stickiness	Sound pressure
Heavy	Synthetic material	Source direction
Humidity	Temperature	Tone
Infection	Tension	Volume

Smell (cont.)	Time	Consciousness
Mint	Literal time	Appetite
Nutty	Suspended time	Cause and effect
Pollution	Expanded moment	Emotional state of others
Pungent	Reality alteration	Emotional state of self
Salty	Time for movement	Physical energy
Smoke	Travel for time	Responsibility
Staleness	Linear time	Right and wrong
Sweetness	Non-linear time	Self-awareness level
Vinegar		
Wood		

Number Symbolism

Choosing numbers that have symbolic meaning and weight can add depth to your narrative. We see it in literature all the time—three little pigs, seven dwarves, etc.

Popular Symbolic Numbers	
Two	Duality, partnership, male & female, yin & yang, left & right, hot & cold, sun & moon, night & day, active & passive, other:
Three	Trinity (Father, Son, & Holy Spirit), circle of life (birth, life, & death), idea of self (mind, body, & spirit), mystical number in folktales (three wishes, three challenges, three guesses, etc.), three rulers in Greek mythology (Zeus, Hades, & Poseidon), three Fates, Shakespeare's *Macbeth* has three witches, other:
Four	Four elements (earth, air, wind, & fire), four cardinal points (north, south, east, & west), humanity (four limbs), four seasons, four humors (blood, choler, phlegm, & black bile), four phases of the moon, four horsemen of the Apocalypse, other:
Six	Satan, evil, the devil (666 is the Biblical "mark of the devil"), other:
Seven	Trinity plus humanity (3+4), days of the week, seven deadly sins, other:
Nine	Nine lives of a cat, Norse mythology there are nine worlds, Greek mythology there are nine Muses, other:
Twelve	A complete cycle, twelve months, twelve hours, twelve disciples of Christ, twelve tribes of Israel, twelve inches in a foot, other:
Thirteen	Unlucky, bad luck, Judas was the thirteenth person to arrive to the last supper, other:
Forty	Trials and tribulations, Hebrews wandered for forty years, other:
Notes:	

Tastes and Aromas

When you are writing, try to incorporate all four of the senses in your work. Here is a cheat sheet for tastes and smells:

Positive	Neutral	Negative	Spices	Florals (Most Fragrant)
Aromatic	Acidic	Biting	Cajun	Angel's Trumpet
Citrusy	Acrid	Bitter	Cinnamon	Flowering Plum
Comforting	Airy	Decay	Clove	Heliotrope
Crisp	Ancient	Dirty	Coriander	Honeysuckle
Delicate	Brackish	Fetid	Cumin	Jasmin
Delicious	Burnt	Foul	Dill	Lavender
Exquisite	Delicate	Funky	Pepper	Lilac
Fragrant	Feminine	Gamy	Sage	Mexican Orange
Fresh	Fermented	Harsh	Thyme	Mock Orange
Fruity	Masculine	Moldy	Basil	Rose
Full-Bodied	Floral	Musty	Barbeque	Star Magnolia
Hard	Humid	Nasty	Bay Leaf	Sweet Peas
Heady	Light	Noxious	Curry	Tuberose
Juicy	Medicinal	Old	Anise	**Household Smells**
Lemony	Medium	Pungent	Caraway Seed	
Rich	Mellow	Putrid	Cardamom	Babies
Savory	Metallic	Rancid	Cayenne	"Boy" Smell
Sharp	Mild	Rank	Cumin	Bacon
Succulent	Minty	Repulsive	Dill	BBQ
Sugary	Moist	Rotting	Fennel	Beer
Sweet	Musky	Skunky	Garlic	Books
Tangy	Nippy	Sour	Ginger	Bread
Tart	Nutty	Spoiled	Mace	Burning Wood
Tempting	Peppery	Stagnant	Marjoram	Chocolate
Warm	Perfumed	Stale	Mint	Cinnamon
Woody	Salty	Stench	Mustard	Citrus
Zesty	Woodsy	Stinking	Onion	Coconut
Zingy	Yeasty	Stuffy	Orange Peel	Coffee
			Lemon Peel	Cut Grass
Other:	Other:	Other:	Nutmeg	Dirty Laundry
			Rosemary	Fresh–Baked Cookies
			Saffron	Fresh Laundry
			Turmeric	Pine
			Vanilla	Soap

Synonyms

As you are editing, it is important to pay attention to repetition. Much of the tinkering with words will come with editing, but I love using synonym sheets to cut down on the editing later, as well as to inspire me.

Emotions

Other words for **Happy**

Alluring, amused, appealing, appeased, blissful, blithe, carefree, charmed, cheeky, chipper, chirpy, content, convivial, delighted, elated, electrified, ecstatic, enchanted, enthusiastic, exultant, excited, fantastic, fulfilled, glad, gleeful, glowing, gratified, idyllic, intoxicating, jolly, joyful, joyous, jovial, jubilant, light, lively, merry, mirthful, overjoyed, pleased, pleasant, radiant, sparkling, savoured, satisfied, serene, sunny, thrilled, tickled, up, upbeat, winsome, wonderful.

Other words for **SAD**

Aching, agitated, anguished, anxious, bleak, bothered, brooding, bugged, chagrined, cheerless, darkly, disillusioned, disappointed, disenchanted, disheartened, dismayed, distraught, dissatisfied, despondent, doleful, failed, faint, frustrated, glazed, gloomy, glowering, haunted, hopeless, languid, miserable, pained, perturbed, sour, suffering, sullen, thwarted, tormented, troubled, uneasy, unsettled, upset, vacant, vexed, wan, woeful, wounded.

Other words for **Mad**

Affronted, aggravated, agitated, angered, annoyed, bitter, boiling, bothered, brooding, bugged, bummed, cantankerous, chafed, chagrined, crabby, cross, disgruntled, distraught, disturbed, enflamed, enraged, exasperated, fiery, fuming, furious, frantic, galled, goaded, hacked, heated, hostile, hot, huffy, ill-tempered, incensed, indignant, inflamed, infuriated, irate, ireful, irritated, livid, maddened, malcontent, miffed, nettled, offended, peeved, piqued, provoked, raging, resentful, riled, scowling, sore, sour, stung, taut, tense, tight, troubled, upset, vexed, wrathful.

Other words for **Crying**

Bawling, blubbering, gushing, howling, lamenting, moaning, scream-crying, silent tears, sniffling, snivelling, sobbing, sorrowing, teary, wailing, weepy, woeful.

Commonly Used Words

Other words for ASKED

Appealed, begged, beckoned, beseeched, besieged, bid, craved, commanded, claimed, coaxed, challenged, charged, charmed, cross-examined, demanded, drilled, entreated, enchanted, grilled, implored, imposed, interrogated, invited, invoked, inquired, insisted, needled, ordered, pleaded, petitioned, picked, probed, pried, pressed, pumped, pursued, put through the wringer, put the screws down, questioned, queried, quizzed, requested, required, requisitioned, roasted, solicited, summoned, surveyed, sweated, urged, wanted, wheedled, wooed, worried, wondered.

Other words for LAUGH

Break up, burst, cackle, chortle, chuckle, crack-up, crow, giggle, grin, guffaw, hee-haw, howl, peal, quack, roar, scream, shriek, snicker, snigger, snort, split one's sides, tee-hee, titter, whoop.

Other Words for LOOK

Address, admire, attention, audit, babysit, beam, beholding, blink, bore, browse, burn, cast, check, comb, consider, contemplate, delve, detect, discover, disregard, distinguish, ensure, evil eye, examine, explore, eye, eyeball, ferret, fix, flash, forage, gander, gaze, get an eyeful, give the eye, glance, glare, glaze, glimmer, glimpse, glitter, gloat, goggle, grope, gun, have a gander, inquire, inspect, investigate, judge, keeping watch, leaf-through, leer, lock daggers on, look fixedly, look-see, marking, moon, mope, neglect, note, notice, noting, observe, ogle, once-over, peek, peep, peer, peg, peruse, poke into, scan, pout, probe, pry, quest, rake, recognize, reconnaissance, regard, regarding, renew, resemble, review, riffle, rubberneck, rummage, scan, scowl, scrutinize, search, seeing, sense, settle, shine, sift, simper, size-up, skim, slant, smile, smirk, snatch, sneer, speculative, spot, spy, squint, stare, study, sulk, supervise, surveillance, survey, sweep, take stock of, take in, trace, verify, view, viewing, watch, witness, yawp, zero in.

Other words for REPLIED

Acknowledged, answered, argued, accounted, barked, bit, be in touch, boomeranged, comeback, countered, conferred, claimed, denied, echoed, feedback, fielded the question, get back to, growled, matched, parried, reacted, reciprocated, rejoined, responded, retorted, remarked, returned, retaliated, shot back, snapped, squelched, squared, swung, vacillated.

Other words for Sat

Be seated, bear on, cover, ensconce, give feet a rest, grab a chair, have a place, have a seat, hunker, install, lie, park, perch, plop down, pose, posture, put it there, relax, remain, rest, seat, seat oneself, settle, squat, take a load off, take a place, take a seat.

Other words for Was/Were   VERB (TO BE)

Abided, acted, be alive, befell, breathed, continued, coexisted, do, endured, ensued, existed, had been, happened, inhabited, lasted, lived, moved, obtained, occurred, persisted, prevailed, remained, rested, stood, stayed, survived, subsided, subsisted, transpired.

Other words for Walk

Advance, amble, barge, bolt, bounce, bound, canter, charge, crawl, creep, dance, dash, escort, gallop, hike, hobble, hop, jog, jump, leap, limp, lope, lumber, meander, mosey, move, pad, pace march, parade, patrol, plod, prance, proceed, promenade, prowl, race, roam, rove, run, sashay, saunter, scamper, scramble, zip shuffle, skip, slink, slither, slog, sprint, stagger, step, stomp, stride, stroll, strut, stumble, swagger, thread, tiptoe, traipse, tramp, tread, trek, trip, trot, trudge, wade, wander.

Other words for Whisper

Breathed, buzz, disclosed, exhaled, expressed, fluttered, gasped, hint, hiss, hum, hushed tone, intoned, lament, low voice, moaned, mouthed, mumble, murmur, mutter, puff, purred, reflected, ruffle, rumble, rush, said low, said softly, sigh, sob, undertone, utter, voiced, wheezed.

Other words for Went

Abscond, ambled, approached, avoided, be off, beat it, bolted, bounced, bounded, bugged out, burst, carved, cleared out, crawled, crept, cruised, cut and run, danced, darted, dashed, decamped, deserted, disappeared, ducked out, escaped, evaded, exited, fared, fled, floated, flew, flew the coop, galloped, got away, got going, got lost, glided, go down, go south, hightailed, hit the road, hoofed it, hopped, hotfooted, hurdled, hustled, journeyed, jumped, leapt, left, lighted out, loped, lunged, made haste, made a break for it, made for, made off, made tracks, marched, moseyed, moved, muscled, neared, negotiated, paced, paraded, passed, pedalled, proceeded, progressed, pulled out, pulled, pushed off, pushed on, quitted, retired, retreated, rode, ran along, ran away, rushed, sashayed, scampered, scooted, scrammed, scurried, scuttled, set off, set out, shot, shouldered, shoved off, shuffled, skedaddled, skipped out, skipped, skirted, slinked, slipped, soared, split, sprang, sprinted, stole away, steered clear, stepped on it, strolled, strutted, scurried, swept, took a hike, took a powder, took flight, took leave, took off, threaded, toddled, tottered, trampled, travelled, traversed, trekked, trode, trudged, tumbled, vamoosed, vanished, vaulted, veered, walked off, wandered, weaved, wended, whisked, withdrew, wormed, zipped, zoomed.

Other words for SAID

Accused, acknowledged, added, announced, addressed, admitted, advised, affirmed, agreed, asked, avowed, asserted, answered, apologized, argued, assured, approved, articulated, alleged, attested, barked, bet, bellowed, babbled, begged, bragged, began, bawled, bleated, blurted, boomed, broke in, bugged, boasted, bubbled, beamed, burst out, believed, brought out, confided, crowed, coughed, cried, congratulated, complained, conceded, chorused, concluded, confessed, chatted, convinced, chattered, cheered, chided, chimed in, clucked, coaxed, commanded, cautioned, continued, commented, called, croaked, chuckled, claimed, choked, chortled, corrected, communicated, claimed, contended, criticized, construe,

dared, decided, disagreed, described, disclosed, drawled, denied, declared, demanded, divulged, doubted, denied, disputed, dictated, echoed, ended, exclaimed, explained, expressed, enunciated, expounded, emphasized, formulated, fretted, finished, gulped, gurgled, gasped, grumbled, groaned, guessed, gibed, giggled, greeted, growled, grunted, hinted, hissed, hollered, hypothesized, inquired, imitated, implied, insisted, interjected, interrupted, intoned, informed, interpreted, illustrated, insinuated, jeered, jested, joked, justified, lied, laughed, lisped, maintained, muttered, marveled, moaned, mimicked, mumble, modulated, murmured, mused, mentioned, mouthed, nagged, noted, nodded, noticed,

objected, observed, offered, ordered, owned up, piped, pointed out, panted, pondered, praised, prayed, puzzled, proclaimed, promised, proposed, protested, purred, pled, pleaded, put in, prevailed, parried, pressed, put forward, pronounced, pointed out, prescribed, popped off, persisted, protested, questioned, quavered, quipped, quoted, queried, rejected, reasoned, ranted, reassured, reminded, responded, recalled, returned, requested, roared, related, remarked, replied, reported, revealed, rebutted, retorted, repeated, reckoned, remembered, regarded, recited, resolved, reflected, ripped, rectified, reaffirmed,

snickered, sniffed, smirked, snapped, snarled, shot, sneered, sneezed, started, stated, stormed, sobbed, stuttered, suggested, surmised, sassed, sputtered, sniffled, snorted, spoke, stammered, squeaked, sassed, scoffed, scolded, screamed, shouted, sighed, smiled, sang, shrieked, shrilled, speculated, supposed, settled, solved, shot back, swore, stressed, spilled, told, tested, trilled, taunted, teased, tempted, theorized, threatened, tore, uttered, unveiled, urged, upheld, vocalized, voiced, vindicated, volunteered, vowed, vented, verbalized, warned, wailed, went on, wept, whimpered, whined, wondered, whispered, worried, warranted, yawned, yakked.

My Synonym Lists:

Other Notes & Research

Books by Robin Woods

Fiction

Allure: A Watcher Series Prequel

The Nexus: The Watcher Series Book Two

The Fallen: Part One: Watcher Series Book Four

The Unintended: The Watcher Series Book One

The Sacrifice: The Watcher Series Book Three

The Fallen: Part Two: Watcher Series Book Five

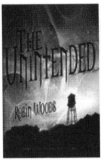     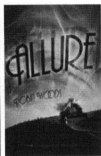

Non-Fiction

Fiction Writing Workbook & Journal

Prompt Me More Workbook & Journal

Prompt Me Workbook & Journal

Prompt Me Sci-Fi & Fantasy Workbook & Journal

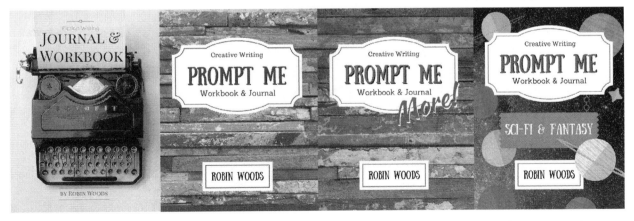

More Prompt Me Series in 2019: *Prompt Me Romance, Prompt Me Kids, Prompt Me Classroom* and more.

Robin Woods is a high school and university instructor with over two decades of experience teaching English, literature, and writing. She earned a BA in English and an MA in education.

In addition to teaching, Robin Woods has published six highly rated novels and has multiple projects in the works, including writing for a Hollywood producer.

When Ms. Woods isn't teaching or writing, she is chasing her two elementary school kids around and spending time with her ever-patient husband.

For more information and free resources, go to her website at:

www.RobinWoodsFiction.com

36742059R00096

Made in the USA
Lexington, KY
17 April 2019